INVISIBLE

Nathalie von Bismarck

INVISIBLE

Nathalie von Bismarck

A&G, LLC
200 East 94 Street, PH 17
New York, NY 10128

978-0-615-41194-1

Layout: Julia Jund, Munich
Illustrations: Nathalie Gräfin von Bismarck

Printed in Canada

"And now here is my secret, a very simple secret;
it is only with the heart that one can see rightly,
what is essential is invisible to the eye."

Antoine de Saint-Exupéry

Man and woman meet, fall in love, get married and boom—one year later, the wife gets pregnant. That's me.

Same old story, right? Well, not quite.

For me it was a love story in the spirit of fairy tales when I met my very own prince charming, well almost … Count Charming. Count Carl-Eduard von Bismarck, the future Prince of Bismarck.

Everybody who knows him calls him Calle. Calle is the great-great grandson of the German statesman Otto Eduard Leopold von Bismarck, known as the Iron Chancellor. My husband's great-great grandfather was largely responsible for the creation of the German Empire in the 1800s. Like the Kennedy family in the U.S., the von Bismarcks are a public political family.

Our relationship happened fast. Calle and I married in September 2004, less than a year after we met. Suddenly I had the responsibilities of being a countess and representing one of Germany's royal families. Society was eager to get a peek at my husband and me. I was eager to be a good wife and fulfill my new duties.

Ever since I could remember, things came easily for me. I got many breaks, doors opened without me knowing, or questioning my luck. I had been blessed with good looks. But I basically took the whole thing for granted, thinking it was completely normal and that everyone was catered to like me. I assumed that this was how life was for

Calle and My Wedding, September 2004

everyone. Today, when I look back, I realize how completely oblivious I'd been.

It is true, appearance and beauty were two of my priorities in life. Growing up, I have always been treated as special, well-liked by men and women—and let me repeat "by men" again.

Previously, I had turned heads and been exposed to the limelight quite a few times. But after my marriage to a count—now I had become a countess—the attention on the red carpet was intense. I was entering a world that was far more judgmental than before.

I must confess, on the surface I was quite modest, shy, and confident but inside I was vain, insecure, and not always compassionate. Like a lot of insecure people, my modesty didn't keep me from judging others. I was not particularly sensitive to anyone hat society labeled unappealing. In college, I hung a sign outside my dorm-room door that said: "The more people I meet, the more I like my dog" with a big photo of my dog attached to it.

This new-found media attention after my marriage could have caused my vanity to grow but instead the only thing that grew was my body.

This is my story of learning the biggest lesson in my life or, I think, in any person's life. Some people might call it a punishment, a lesson from God, or just an eye opener. But whatever you want to call it, the point is that it made such an impact and a difference in my life that it

In the Spotlight

completely changed me, how I am, and how I see people and life forever.

Let me explain how I fell over the divide that separates thin and fat, visible and invisible, cruel and kind, and how a new appreciation for life poured in.

During our first year of marriage there didn't seem to be enough hours in the day. My husband and I were hopping from country to country, looking forward to the next event. New faces kept appearing—each more important than the last. People were accommodating my every whim and desire. On the outside it might sound like I lived a fantasy and to an extent that is true, but it does get tiresome quickly. I asked my new husband to slow down our commitments. I was exhausted. I craved sleep.

I soon found out why I was so tired. We were expecting a baby!

We were ecstatic. We decided to keep our expectancy secret—keeping the first months private from the press. With me so slender, we thought it would go unnoticed. Immediately, I did what all dutiful, expectant mothers do. I watched what I ate and kept an eye on the scale. I cut out fried and fatty foods and my favorites—hot dogs and goat cheese. For me, no sacrifice was too much for my baby.

And my pregnancy did go unnoticed, at least temporarily. At the beginning, standing shy of six feet tall, I weighed in at just 125 pounds. I knew the first pregnancy would be a a shock to the body.

La Dolce Vita

But the shock I didn't expect was that in those nine months I'd double in size.

Naturally, I assumed I'd be like one of those pregnant celebrities who, no matter what they ate, with or without exercise, stayed skinny. You know who I am talking about. You've seen them plastered on magazines. Those perfect creatures with the adorable baby bumps that look like a balloon attached with a rope to their little teeny, tiny waists. Those women, who if you stood behind them, you would not know were pregnant! And, mysteriously, one week after they've given birth, they're back on magazine covers wearing nothing else but a bikini and a big smile, while showing off their bundles of joy. On the cover, the headline blares, "How X lost the weight!" What weight?

Reality Bites

And then there was me, the un-
heard of, of course me! Who else?
As careful as I was when I got pregnant, I was expanding and retaining
water like a blow fish.

In the first two couple of months, I
easily put on twenty pounds. It was
a big leap for my small frame, but
the weight gain wasn't too
bad. Obviously, my pregnancy was
no longer a secret. Friends and
family were thrilled. Well wishes
raced in, "Oh, you are pregnant. You
are starting to show, filling in a bit,
aren't we?" I often heard, "That's
healthy, that's really good for the
baby," everyone insisted.

As my body morphed from thin to voluptuous, my husband and I were enjoying the first three months of my pregnancy. I was lucky. Other than feeling dizzy sometimes, I managed to sidestep morning sickness. More than that, I can't really say because I slept a lot. I just wanted to sleep and sleep and then sleep some more. To keep up with our long list of engagements, I'd sneak in naps.

In no time the word "weight watching" was tossed out the window and in came the appetite. I was eating for two after all, right? But soon my clothes started feeling tighter on me. Pants and skirt zippers were harder and harder to close. Buttons popped off. Everything I owned reached its maximum giving point. My ankles and feet swelled like balloons. Now I could only stand next to my beautiful shoes. Rings? Forget it.

I couldn't wear any of them, not even my wedding band. All these changes were natural during pregnancy, but they were happening far too soon. I panicked, I worried. I couldn't believe it when within five months into my pregnancy the scale leaped sixty pounds. That's right. I gained sixty pounds. A red light alert switch went on and a panic and worry marked my face because that's the weight most women might gain in nine months not five. Something must be wrong.

Already I looked ready to pop. I was always extreme and different in everything I did in my life; it goes hand in hand with my extreme personality. But did that have to apply in pregnancy as well? The extra weight was taking its toll. I was having trouble walking. My back was cracking, my knees ached from the massive weight they suddenly had to carry but it would get worse, much, much worse.

Going Bananas

I started feeling depressed. "Why," I asked myself with self-pity. Why do I have to be the one in a million? Why can't I be like other mothers-to-be who glow? Was I allergic to being pregnant?

I learned very quickly that the notion of "a glowing beautiful pregnant woman" wasn't normal; the truth is most pregnant women feel horrible, especially during the last trimester. Any woman who says differently is simply not telling the truth or is in a high level of denial.

But my rapid weight gain was far out of the norm. Even though I was pregnant, I looked obese. My pregnancy weight spread all over my body as opposed to being confined only to my belly. By looking at me, people couldn't tell if I was pregnant or just huge.

I constantly went to see my doctor. He was one of the best and had seen it all—or so he thought. But, when he saw me, his face grew serious and his eyebrows furrowed tightly together. Then he showed great concern and what I took to be fear. I will never forget his face when he said, "This is not normal! You are not normal!" My doctor said he had never seen a woman retain so much water weight and spill sugar.

He worried about my health and my life. Serious concerns of pregnancy diabetes and heart failure topped the list of scary pregnancy issues. I was terrified for my baby and for my myself.

My doctor questioned me tirelessly about my diet, certain it must be the reason why I was gaining so much weight. Repeatedly I told him how I was eating healthy and unlike other pregnant women, I didn't have cravings for potato chips or even pickles.

Okay, wait, fine, if I am being completely candid here, I did have one craving—bananas. I ate a lot of them, but surely bananas couldn't be the culprit, could they? No, no matter what I ate, my weight gain was escalating out of control.

I must admit one more thing. One afternoon, I was busted. During a moment of weakness, I had inhaled a divine chocolate brownie on my way to see the doctor. It was easy for him to catch me, like a little girl who made a boo boo, because of the spike in my test results. But I swear, that was my only indulgence and truly it was.

Stepping out of the doctor's office later that day, a solid 185 pounds, I didn't know what was happening to me, but I was aware of what was happening around me.

This is what I would like to share with you; to tell you about society, stigma and stereotype, humiliation and humility, hypocrisy, truth and more.

As I walked home, I quickly realized how people were so blinded by beauty, and how they got it all wrong. It is shallow, isn't it? We all like compliments and I had always been showered with them. But by the end of six months into my pregnancy, I noticed heads were once again turning, but this time in the other direction.

When I used to walk down the street at 125 pounds, I kid you not when I tell you that at least four or five heads would turn, give me a look, and scan me from head to toe. When I was thin, if I would accidentally drop my keys, someone would rush up and pick them up for me before I could blink. If I lugged a heavy bag to my house, a neighbor or anyone passing in the hallway would offer to help me and carry the bag. People were more willing to help me whether I needed help or not.

Sometimes after I had paid for my groceries, after standing in a supermarket line, the owner would come out of his window office, hurry down the stairs, grab a product, put it in my grocery bag with a big smile, and say, "This is for you, for free!" You should have seen the look on my face whenever that happened. Each one of us has that rare moment where you don't know what the hell to say. That was one of mine. I smiled and nodded with my head as a "thank you." But as a big fat obese woman, no way.

Nobody would give an obese person the time of day.

Now that I was obese, pregnant, and suffering from health problems, no one looked, no one cared, and no one helped. I was invisible.

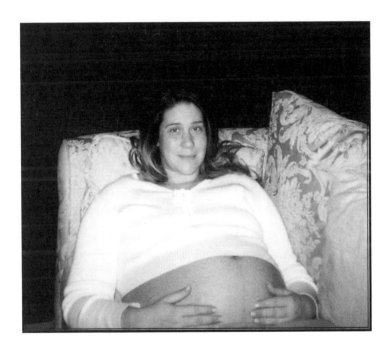

Not only would they ignore me, it was as if I didn't exist. Within a few short months, I had become an obstacle to bypass, not a person worth the time of day.

I was about to learn the lesson of my life. Vanity was the first to go. Suddenly nothing was more important than my health. My ego was already flushed down the toilet, as I was pushed around, ignored, mistreated, and more.

Something strange happened during my pregnancy that I never imagined was possible. My husband was shrinking in front of my eyes. The bigger I became the smaller he was becoming next to me. At this rate, I feared I might make him disappear if I hugged him.

And sex. Forget it! Throw that sweet thought right out the window. I couldn't risk squashing him. My embarrassment and discomfort in my own skin, my incredible expanding body, made that impossible. There was no way I wanted him to touch me.

At six months, I had incurred some minor accidents but luckily nothing threatening to my child.

There was one night, for example, when my husband and I left a party with some good friends, a couple, who were both beautiful inside and out.

There was a cable wire lying across the ground. Everyone passed it without a problem, except me. With my weak, trembling, and cracked knees, I tripped and fell to the ground. Lately, I had been falling a lot, and my husband, who knew the depth of my health problems, took my fall very seriously. He immediately helped me up. But the other couple didn't know what I had been going through. For the most part they reacted with small giggles combined with concern. I basically didn't know how to respond.

I could either let my feelings get hurt or not take it personally because I knew they didn't mean to offend me. I chose to ignore it and be happy.

My condition was hindering my ability to walk on my own. Somehow—I don't know how—my incredibly shrinking husband had turned into my human cane.

I could see Calle was starting to get scared; my health was deteriorating quickly. We were both scared. I know I am the glue in this relationship, someone always is. I had to keep it together. I couldn't let fear take over.

There he was with me, day in, day out, everywhere I had to go, keeping me from falling, tripping, or steadying me whenever I got dizzy. He helped me on the street, getting into cars, out of cars, up the stairs, down the stairs. Not to forget, he helped me get to the toilet, and from the toilet. The list was long. It became a nightmare, physically and mentally. I felt numb in my heart and crippled.

Like all parents-to-be, Calle and I had a lot to do before the baby's arrival. One day, we went to take care of errands. Maneuvering through crowds became increasingly difficult. The worst part for me was dodging the looks people gave me. For the most part, people looked right past me as if I were invisible. To others it was as though I wasn't physically there.

Now, I was being bumped, and pushed out of the way with their elbows because they were in a rush without as much as an "excuse me," or smile as a gesture of a slight apology.

Do you see something wrong with this picture? I sure do; the fact is when it comes to outer appearance people lose the human aspect. It doesn't make sense because it is big women who are the ones who need help. Beauty blinds so many people. The irony was the bigger I became, the more I disappeared.

What hurt the most weren't strangers ignoring me, during the many sad days I had at the time, but people I actually knew. I would see them as I walked down the street or ate at a restaurant, but they couldn't or wouldn't see me. I don't think all of them were snubbing me, many really, absolutely 100 percent did not recognize me!

I was registered in people's heads as a completely different person. When I would confront them and say, "Hey, it's me Nathalie," there would always be a second of pause … thinking … confused … registering … digesting … and the "Ah!"

This was followed by a strange smile. "Hey, Nathalie! You're pregnant. Oh my God! I never would have recognized you."

I tell you that response was always there. It never failed to occur with all the people I ran into. I felt horrible, not just for me. I actually, oddly enough, would think about their feelings and not my own. How awkward and embarrassing they must have felt caught off guard like that. Well, I can't really blame them.

As I'd walk away, I'd think to myself, "It's okay. It's temporary. They'll be just as shocked when I am back to being skinny." But little did I know then that what I was going through would change me forever.

Then there were the "friends" who expected me to explain why I let this happen to myself. For those people, I managed to smile straight through. But good things have come out of it. It helped me realize who really loved the beauty inside of me.

I was quickly learning that we live in an amazing world that's so stereotyped. The same people who couldn't get enough of me and my energy turned out to be utterly ruthless. I felt sociological pain as a result of some of those experiences. It was crippling me to the bone. The mental and verbal abuse affected me so badly that there were times I lost the will to get dressed, and I'd stay in my pjs all day. I didn't want to talk on the phone, not to friends or relatives either. I stayed in bed most of the day and sunk into a deep depression.

My husband, however, took all the changes happening to me in stride. He didn't once complain about the public humiliation he suffered as people joked about his incredibly-enlarging wife behind our backs. But I could see the changing ways he looked at me. As my condition worsened, he worried I might break.

When I got pregnant, Calle did not know he would, nor ask to be taking care of a wife with disabilities who was nearly crippled. One time, when he was being so sweet, supporting, and understanding, his face changed to worried, to very worried. He gently and very quietly asked me, "But ... but ... honey, you won't stay like this, right? It's a condition due to your pregnancy and will all go away, right?" Now what the hell am I supposed to say to that while I am hormonal, in pain all over with aching bones in my body? I think my knee caps might pop off.

Of course, it's due to my pregnancy! You $@%.

I wanted to punch him really hard between the eyes, but instead I bit my tongue, holding back tears. Seeing my eyes swell up, he quickly backtracked, "Oh, it's okay. You're so beautiful right now, just in that pregnant kind of way. It's that kind of beauty." He blurted on. Yeah, right. In that pregnant kind of way.

At that point, I gave up on the whole conversation. My husband meant well, but he is a terrible liar.

I was in the middle of my seventh month of pregnancy and my husband's birthday was around the corner. For weeks, I'd successfully avoided most of my obligations. I was concerned the media would skewer me if they saw how huge I was getting. At the same time, I wanted to celebrate Calle's birthday. He had been going through this difficult experience with me, so I decided to throw him a big party. God knows where I found the strength.

I decided to have his birthday in St. Moritz, Switzerland, where my husband grew up skiing. It's the playground for everyone who is anyone. I don't know what I was thinking. It was like throwing myself in with a pack of hungry wolves ... St. Moritz, here I come.

The night before the party I arranged a small dinner for a few close friends. I remember standing nervously in the entrance to greet them with my husband. I couldn't believe it when I saw I was taking up most of the space in the doorway. He barely had room to stand. When our guests arrived, their mouths dropped.

Out of Breath

Remember, these were well-educated people with all their social graces and skills. Yet there was no way to hide their disbelief at the physical changes I had undergone.

At dinner, I sat on the inside of the long table armed with my good friends. Unfortunately, I realized too late that sitting on the inside required pushing the table so far out to make room for my ready-to-pop belly that our guests could barely reach the bread in the middle of the table. That night, as you can imagine, I didn't sleep soundly.

At the first sign of the morning light, I went to the lodge to be sure everything for Calle's birthday party was conducted to my liking. When everything was ready, I left to get myself dressed for the night. It was a theme party; I didn't have much of a costume but I managed to throw something together.

When the guests began to arrive, most of them didn't recognize me; others who did were speechless. I spent most of the evening watching all the beautiful people having the time of their life.

In my society, obesity is not tolerated.

Toward the end of the evening, my husband got up. As he gave a heartfelt speech thanking me, the spotlight was on me. He came over to give me a hug. I was embarrassed when his arms couldn't get around me. Thankfully, the spotlight dimmed and the party was winding down.

Potato Snacks are Pretty

Previously, I had been very active and an athletic, can you imagine the mental and physical humiliation of not being able to climb a small, snowy mountain in St. Moritz? I know, I know, wrong place for a seven month pregnant women to be....

That's what happened the next day.

Luckily for me, one of our friends, the most handsome and strongest man in our group, was so sweet and kind to offer me help, not knowing what he was getting himself into. You should have seen him; by the time we reached the top of the mountain, he looked like he just carried up a bulldozer. Can you imagine what that ordeal did to my ego at that moment? I didn't know whether to laugh or cry.

Shopping was the last thing on my mind, but my girlfriend insisted we go to cheer me up because nothing but a potato sack fit me anymore.

When my girlfriend and I arrived at the department store we were in for a shock. I must have been clueless because I never realized before how all the clothes were made for Barbie dolls. Even though I tried on all the biggest sizes, I couldn't get my hands on anything that worked. Nothing at all ... zippo. As the desperation appeared on our faces, a sweet salesgirl gently suggested we try looking downstairs.

We descended down, down, and down several floors to the basement. It was fashion exile; where no designers dared to go.

We were banished to a whole different world. We instantly realized that most designers don't cater to big women. Designer clothes come in small, medium, and large; anything bigger than that is not the same design and not as attractive. I couldn't understand looking at these outfits, why is it that when the size goes up, the design and quality of the clothes appear to go down? Why can't they make pretty clothes bigger?

Suddenly my potato sack wasn't looking so bad anymore.

When we ran out of the department store, it was one of the few times I was light on my feet since I got pregnant.

Speaking of clothes, some designers used to send me beautiful dresses and outfits, as they knew I might wear them during a public appearance. When I gained weight, nothing was sent to me, they simply stopped sending me clothes. Talk about brutal. Today the same designers try to send me things to reconnect. Let's just say, I actually like to make humor of it, so I wear their competitors' designs.

At eight months into my pregnancy, my husband and I were enjoying a beautiful day in Santa Monica, California with a couple of guests at our house. It was lunchtime. Everyone was hungry, so I suggested we get something nice and easy like grabbing a hamburger or sandwich. We had heard about Johnny Rockets, known for its feel-good easy diner food. We thought we'd give it a try.

It was our first time there, ever. I saw "house burger" on the menu. I assumed it was their speciality—so it must be very good—and so I ordered it.

What I didn't know was that at Johnny Rockets the house burger was really, really special. So special because it would feed ten people not one. It also came with a side-order of a ritual. I had no idea.

A loud commotion broke out. I looked up and saw that our waiter was the commotion. I couldn't believe it because he was headed toward me.

In one hand our waiter was ringing a bell like a wild man while carrying a burger as big as a football in the other. Firecrackers that were sticking out of it went off. Everyone in the restaurant started clapping and hooting.

All eyes stared at the humongous burger as our waiter made his way straight to humongous me.

As he drew closer, I heard it. It was the moment of judgment about my appearance. Fingers started wagging like tisk, tisk. Some of the cheers turned into snickers as a few people wondered out loud as to why such an obese woman would order this massive meal.

Was she trying to give herself a heart attack? Our jaws hit the floor. My husband and our friends were horrified by the clapping, cheers, sneers and ringing bells, all growing louder and louder. Finally, the waiter stopped in front of me.

With great showmanship, he plunked the giant burger down on the table right in front of my face with the sparkles still twinkling. The restaurant exploded in a final round of applause. It was so loud that it nearly blew my ear drums out. I wanted to go poof and vanish into thin air. I tried to slip under the table, but at my size, that was impossible.

I was so humiliated. Then I couldn't help it. People were going to judge me regardless of what I did or ate, and I burst into laughter. It was just so absurd and hysterical at the same time.

It was a summer day in New York City when I realized that not only was it a burden for me to get around but it was a burden for other people to get me around.

I needed to get from one place to another but there were no yellow cabs in sight. I spotted a group of pedicab drivers and headed towards them. When I was skinny, pedicab drivers used to line up. "Hey lady, need a ride?" Now they scattered and ran for their lives.
I managed to stop one pedicab driver, a strapping man. He looked me up and down and turned me down flat.

The second driver, a skinny, little man showed me some compassion. He agreed to take me. I felt awful for him after I hauled myself up, nearly knocked his cart over before I settled myself in a space meant for two people.

The driver, like Hercules, tried to pull me through the busy Manhattan streets. His behind was raised off the seat as he pushed hard on the bicycle pedals. His toothpick legs were pumping with all of their might to get me to my destination. I couldn't help but notice the stream of sweat that turned to puddles racing down his back. I really needed the ride, but I was afraid this trip with me might be the end of him.

I was days away from giving birth and I weighed in at 245 pounds. Everyone, including my doctor, was scared for me. It was strange because by then I was going through a calm phase. I was much more relaxed than my friends and family. I tried my best to take all of this with a bit of grace and a whole lot of humor, as I was so confident that I would not stay like this forever. I even made jokes about it, just to keep going and not break down. I knew I had to endure while I kept my head up through so many humiliations.

I knew I was in the final stretch. But seeing people's facial expressions and awkward behavior when they saw me certainly didn't help lift my spirits. I had to not let people around me feel uncomfortable by pretending I was not aware of what they must be thinking about me.

The odd time I caught a glimpse of my reflection in the mirror I'd do a double take. Do you remember the movie *Star Wars*? One of the main characters went by the name of Jabba the Hut. Remember? Does that ring a bell? If it does, then you know that he is an enormous creature with many folds and flab with no identifiable shape.

Gravity

That was me; that is what I had become. I kid you not.

My neck, well necks is more like it—all three of them had layers of flesh like a Shar Pei dog. My nose blew up like a water balloon and spread over my face between my eyes which had shrunk and become beauty. Think I am exaggerating? See for yourself!

See the Resemblance?!

Falling from Grace

You know when things are funny, but only in retrospect?

The worst thing that could have happened to me was yet to come. Two weeks before my due date, I could barely move. This is the stage in any pregnancy where women can't take it anymore and want the baby to come out. The only strength I had left was to count the days until I gave birth. I spent most of that time in bed.

Simple things like going to the kitchen to grab a glass of water were a challenge for me; so was going to the bathroom.

But I really, badly had to go to the toilet, hoping I would make it this time. All women who have been pregnant know what I am talking about. It's a fact that your bladder won't hold when you are in the last stages of your pregnancy. So I rolled myself like a sumo wrestler right to the bathroom.

Rushing wildly, I aggressively sat strongly on the toilet seat, dropping all my 245 pounds along with me. Ha! I did it!

But my triumphant moment was short lived.

Out of nowhere, I heard a noise.

Crrraaccckk … ccrrr … crack … .

At first I wondered where the noise was coming from. Then I thought to myself, "Wow!" I am so heavy. The noise must have come from the toilet seat because it's carrying a lot of pressure. Very quickly I realized that was not the case as my thighs started to hurt because of a burning sensation like sharp tweezers were cutting into my legs.

I barely rolled myself up to a squatting position, turned around, stared down at the toilet seat when I gave the loudest, most painful scream ever.

My husband heard my cry. Panicked, he rushed into the bathroom to see his wife in front of him with a cold sweat, crying tears of pain and misery.

"Oh God!" I yelled, "That's it! Please, I want the baby to come out now. I don't want to be fat and pregnant anymore." Wow! Talk about a serious meltdown. At that point I really had had it.

"What happened?" Calle asked.

I just looked at him with streams of tears running down my face and said, "Honey, I have reached rock bottom. I broke the toilet seat. I didn't just crack it or ding it. I literally broke it!"

Through the whole pregnancy, I had held on tight. Now I was melting down remembering, in self pity, how I used to be as I looked at the broken toilet. I used to be beautiful. I was someone people envied. I had it ALL. Now look at me. I am breaking toilet seats and I can't get up by myself!!

Then, like a typical male, my husband looked at the broken toilet seat, then frowned at me and said, "Oh great! Now what am I going to do?"

That night, I sent him to sleep on the couch. Not that there was much space for him in our bed anyway.

Popped

I marched into the hospital like a walking volcano ready to erupt, pushing anyone away that was in my path.

Entering the hospital to give birth was no joke. It was a big—literally a big task for my husband, the nurses, and the doctor.

For my doctor, the big task was his long-term concern for my health. Me? I was hormonal, and fed up with my condition. The nurses were concerned and scared for other reasons. I swear now when I look back, I laugh so hard thinking this was straight out of a comedy movie. I was so hormonal and after nine months of being ignored and treated like an idiot, I had it up to my eyeballs with it all.

The first nurse, who walked into my room, wanted to stick a needle in my arm for the IV. Because of past experiences, I asked her, "Please not in my left arm. I'll turn purple and blue."

The nurse didn't even acknowledge my existence. She just went ahead, sticking the needle into my left arm. Have you ever seen a volcano erupt after keeping hot boiling lava inside for nine months?

Trust me, not a pretty sight. I grabbed the nurse's arm, pushed her away with the needle still half inside me, then yanked it out. I yelled at the top of my lungs, "See, I turn instantly blue! Why doesn't anyone listen to me? Get out of my room! I don't want to see any nurses. Only my doctor.

The nurse turned pale and ran out. Two minutes later another nurse appeared carrying a cup with some pills. I asked her what the pills were because I always like to know what I am about to swallow, when… here we go again… she ignores my questions. "Just take it, ma'am," she tells me.

Now, for the record, this nurse looked pretty tough. I guess after the incident with the first nurse, they sent her in especially to deal with me. I don't think it helped, as I threw the cup with pills at her. She ran out too.

On the one hand, I have never been this impatient or rude to people, but on the other hand, at this point, can you blame me? I was a 245 pound hormonal woman ready to pop, reacting with a short fuse. Thirty minutes later, in comes a third nurse, this time with a metal wee-wee pan. You know the ones where if you are bedridden, it slides under you if you have to go to the bathroom?

That was it. My biggest explosion ever was triggered by a wee-wee pan. Can you believe it? First I told her I could go by myself. I am big and in pain but not crippled.

The nurse insisted. I resisted. She really insisted again, I really resisted again, and then I went kamikaze. I grabbed the pan from her and screamed, "Enough!" As I made a hand gesture, aiming to throw the pan, she ran out of the room. I threw it and luckily missed her head.

The noise of the wee-wee pan smashing to the floor knocked some sense into me. Suddenly, I scared myself as my self-awareness took over. I though, "Nathalie, what's wrong with you? You've never behaved like that!" An hour and a half passed by and no one showed up. Even my husband, who was in the waiting room, knew he'd better stay away. Then my doctor came in and looked at me like I've been a bad girl.

"So, troublemaker, explain this to me: I have the toughest trained nurse team and you manage to scare them."

"Scare them?" I asked.

"Yes," my doctor replied. "The nurses refuse to come in now. Whoever walks in runs out."

I quietly told my story to my doctor in a very relaxed manner. Finally, someone was really listening to me. He just stood there with a big smile and nodded his head from side to side. From that point onward, my doctor took care of me. I was calm and nice. I even smiled a bit as he attended to me as a human being. My husband, who seems to have a talent for showing up after the "storm," arrived shortly thereafter accompanied by the anesthesiologist. Calle had been explaining to him how extremely sensitive I was to medication.

We thought he was listening. Of course, he wasn't. By then I got used to the idea of being invisible. As a result, right after delivering my

child, my husband had to hold and bottlefeed our beautiful baby boy because mommy was too busy throwing up for eight hours, on and off, a foamy yellow liquid—the anaesthesia. Yep! It happened again—ignored. He didn't even listen and overdosed me with the meds.

Now, this is the big turning point in my life.

Half sedated, eight hours after giving birth, I held my son.

He looked up at me, straight into my eyes, and I looked back at him. At that moment, in a split second, I gained my power and confidence back. There was no greater achievement than this. This was it! Your biggest masterpiece. The whole world as I knew it ceased to exist.

My first pure smile from my son to me gave me hope and enormous strength to deal with anything.

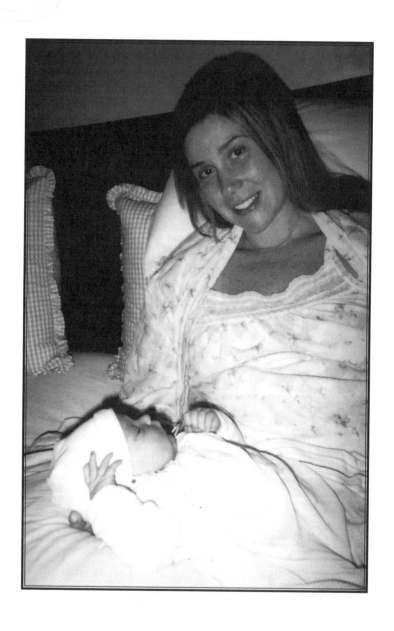

Going home with my husband and son, a few days later, in a wheelchair of course, marked a new beginning for me. Everything from my past that bothered or hurt me was puny and insignificant compared to what I was holding in my arms.

It was good to be home. But I still had a long way to go in my recovery. After giving birth, I had so much weight to lose. I was tied down to a wheelchair. My body had decided to take a vacation without me and I couldn't walk for three months. Walking one block was like running a marathon for me.

But I was slowly feeling better and getting stronger, when my husband and I decided to take a flight to introduce our newborn to the family.

This was my first encounter with the "terrible society," a combination of ignorance and cruelty that can lead to a very dangerous combo. On that trip, we waited at the airport check-in for a wheel chair. It took them forty minutes to get me one.

If you are obese or a big person, society caters to you the wrong way around, in a horrible way that is despicable beyond any words. When the wheelchair finally arrived to bring me to the plane, I couldn't fit in it because it was too small, so they ordered a bigger chair for me and we had to wait even longer. Meanwhile, all the smiles are gone. No one smiles anymore!

Gosh, too many people take life too seriously. It's overrated if you ask me.

But the end result because of the wheelchair fiasco was that we almost missed our flight.

Almost missing our flight was bad enough, especially when you are physically weak, but the worst part was when two flight attendants talked right above my head as if I didn't exist. Could they not tell the difference between someone being mentally crippled and physically crippled? What happened at this point is that they started treating me and talking to me as if I was an idiot or an infant—and that's in a good case scenario.

As I sat right between them they talked about what to do with me as though I couldn't hear them. Even if I attempted to get in a word, or make a suggestion, they didn't listen. They didn't care. I was considered an inanimate piece of wood.

The airline industry isn't built to handle obese people, particularly the planes. The airplane seats are too small. Not only can you not fit in them, the flight attendants have the audacity to tell you, "Well, if it's too small for you and you are not comfortable, then you should buy two full fare seats."

I swear to you I received this remark and "kind advice" not just from one airline but from several others too. In fact, some airlines make you buy two seats.

Then there are the food tray tables. As big as I was, there was no way I could bring the tray down and open it flat halfway. There is no space to back up and the tray would hit me. Now if I were a skinny, beautiful model, not only would the tray be opened for me, it would be opened with a smile from a flight attendant who would accompany it with an extra question, such as: "Would you like some more of this or that? Would you like a lovely glass of champagne to go with that?"

An obese person, no way!

Not only do the flight attendants see you struggling with the bloody tray and not lift a finger to help solve the problem, but they stand right above you, rolling their eyes, puffing their cheeks while they hold the food tray, and say in a very impatient tone, "I will be back when you are ready."

My mouth was left open, ah ... hello ... I guess I will never be ready. I guess I will not be eating on this flight either.

Okay, I know, I could have opened my mouth, made a point, fight back the system—the ignorant, the cruel, and the insensitive, for what?

You see, when you are in such a weak position or crippled you have two choices.

First, you get upset, open your mouth, create a fight and still starve or secondly, you can meditate and say to yourself that their ignorance and problems are not yours. I will not let their bad energy rub off on me and, of course, still starve.

To top it off, after we landed, for thirty-five minutes I had to sit in an empty plane. There is a policy where all the passengers leave first and then those who need assistance go last. Where is the common sense and compassion? The deboarding order makes no sense. It should be the needy who get off first, then the rest.

As time went on, slowly I was walking and smiling more. Immediately I ate healthy and within the first month, I lost a lot of water weight. I couldn't see the light yet, but it was a start. I was determined to go way beyond, as I watched my husband rolling on the floor playing with our baby son, I couldn't help but think, "If I stay this way, I couldn't do that. I couldn't dance or run or play with him." I had to drop the weight for my child, for all of us, and for a happier me.

I also wouldn't want my son to be embarrassed by me in the future. As he grew up, society would eventually rub off on him. So I went on a non-carb diet where I could eat as much as I wanted at any time, (I picked the healthy stuff). But I needed a good, strong head start to get this big diet rolling. Luckily, nearby was a small low-key Buddhist spa clinic that I could go to on a daily basis. I booked myself for a seven-day program. How hard can it be?

After my physical, I was set up in a program that combines yoga, meditation, massages, colonic, health classes and more. The biggest adjustment was I couldn't eat solid foods.

I could only drink protein shakes.

The first day without food, only protein shakes, I was okay and in pretty good spirits. The second day I grew quieter. I could feel other spa-goers at the clinic growing angry. By the third day, I swear I started biting the furniture in the room, hallucinating, having mistaken a chair for a chicken. I was so hungry, but I hung in there.

It was worth it.

After a week of treatments, I felt great. Positive, motivated, five pounds lighter from the colonic, and ten pounds lighter because of the protein shakes, and I had great skin. My head was clear, the pain in my body was disappearing, and my heart was full of love.

The more I was getting my confidence back, the more alive I felt. As they say, step-by-step and day-by-day. I knew this would take a while, but I had made up my mind. Eight months later, I hit 130 pounds. Unbelievably cool, no? I lost it all! But amazingly, something else strange happened.

There were the people who didn't recognize me when I was fat, and then there were those who didn't recognize me when I lost all the baby fat.

Now it was a bit confusing for all these women who were so friendly to me and were not threatened by me when I was big, were now the same women who stared me down and hardly spoke to me once the weight was gone.

Talk about insecure. I made sure that I remained the same person within through it all, big or small.

In the past I would've taken the women who snubbed me after I lost the weight to heart, but after what I experienced, I say Ah! I am so happy to be back, even with the catty women, even with the annoying people on the streets, from construction workers to flirty boys. I welcome them all with a smile. I am not annoyed, angry, or irritated like I was in the past. Now, I take it all with a smile.

Who's that Lady?

The shocked reactions to my weight gain also applied after I lost the weight but in a completely different way. This time the shock was positive. It was my best male friend's fortieth birthday party and I decided to make that night my coming out night. All sleek and skinny, I walked into the party wearing an attractive outfit. I received so many compliments, but an unusual one in particular stuck with me.

It came from one of his best friends, let's just call him G. We met during the later stages of my pregnancy when I was obese. G approached me at the party and showed sincere excitement at how unbelievable I looked, and like many others, he didn't recognize me at first. Then he unintentionally let it slip that when we first met, he couldn't understand why my best male friend, the birthday boy, was friends with me. G couldn't see what my best friend saw in me because beautiful women always accompanied him. Why was I there? Why was I so special to him?

When I heard that, my mouth dropped open. It was perhaps the shallowest statement I have ever heard.

I quickly turned my shock into a smile; however, it was just too much for me to even respond beyond that smile. He meant it as a compliment, so I found it to be sweet.

Then there was another kind of shock. My husband knew this older couple for many years; let's call them the "Hs." He introduced me to them at a few of their dinners where we always shared wonderful conversations about so many interesting things. I always felt that Mr. H liked me for me. He met me when I was obese and he never judged me in any way.

One night I went to a party after I lost the weight and I saw them there. Mrs. H was mingling and socializing at cocktail hour, and her husband was relaxing on the couch. I was so happy to see him, I sat next to him and we talked for a good twenty minutes. But the reaction my skinny self got from him was like the one my fat self brought out in everyone else. He seemed strange and distant. I couldn't help but wonder why

I found out shortly after, at dinner time, why. We both got up and took our seats. Two minutes after I sat down at the table, Mrs. H ran towards me, hysterically laughing.

She told me Mr. H just came and asked who this beautiful woman sitting next to him and chatting with him was.

"Well, that was Countess Nathalie von Bismarck, what, you didn't recognize her?" she said. Mr. H answered, "That can't be her. Nathalie is big, very big. This girl was demure and small, anything but big." When she told me the story I smiled back. I thought to myself, "Wow." I had sat with Mr. H so many times and he didn't recognize me. My outer image really affected his ability to recognize. It was amazing. I decided to take the whole thing as a humorous compliment.

A Few Words of Advice

After my son was born I could no longer hide. I knew my life would be much like it was before. Being married to the future Prince von Bismarck and the mother of the future heir, I'd have to continue my public appearances with my husband. That meant coming out in the media and introducing our son. My son was a crowd-pleaser, his cherub like beauty, and energy satisfied the public more.

I must say, media attention sometimes has its downfalls. Being part of a public political family, it was even harder and more embarrassing for me when photographers took those photos—the "before and after" pictures.

But the best part of my coming out after I had lost all that weight was when some of the magazines that had previously battered me were now surprised I was back having lost the pounds. There were no more comments like "she looks like she's going to burst." Those same magazines now said, "Wow, she lost all of that baby fat."

I learned during that period of my life that it can be an increasingly cruel world.

In the past, I had it all and got it all, but I didn't know what to do with it. Then during my difficult pregnancy I was talking to the trees. Before my pregnancy, I rarely appreciated being catered to and sometimes I even—if you can imagine—was fed up and annoyed by it.

But as my experience proves, at the end of the day be careful what you wish for. As the saying goes: "God gives walnuts to people that have no teeth."

In the past, I was stared at. There were people who would make comments or come on to me; others would be helpful with my luggage or helpful by grabbing me a cab. When I used to walk down the street and a guy would notice me and say something nice, I used to snub him and keep on walking with this annoyed look. Once I was transformed to being obese, I realized that my reality as I knew it and my perspective had completely changed. Heads were no longer turning. There were no smiles, nothing. It was like I didn't exist. Although I was there physically I was invisible.

It is so sad to see society is not fully capable of catering to obese people. I am a living, breathing example of that.

For me, becoming obese during my pregnancy was an unbelievable, indescribable experience. More like an out of body experience. I felt like a small, skinny person trapped in a big, very big person's body. I felt like a monster because I believed it and I was treated like one.

Some people pitied me. Others kept their distance as if I had some kind of contagious disease.

I believe the majority of society is full of "hot air" when it comes to showing how much they care about obese people, how much they will help them, treat them equally and not look at obesity as a freak of nature. Does society really understand them and their needs? Based on my experience, the answer is no. Obese people have feelings and thoughts like everyone else.

No one could ever be the same person after living through this type of experience. The pain, yes, pain, be it sociological or physical, changes a person. In my case the pain was both physical and mental. It was constant. It was so severe from my head to my toes that at many points, it brought me to talk to myself a lot. I grew so used to the pain that I learned how to live with it. Now that the physical pain is gone, I appreciate that my body must be treated with respect like a shrine, but I will never forget the pain and sadness.

The next time you see an obese person, be sensitive to the less fortunate in all aspects. I hope you'll know there is more to them than what you see. Not to mention that society does not cater nor is sensitive to their needs. Don't look the other way, that's the easy way out. We tend to ignore and not deal with things that make us uncomfortable and omit them from our daily reality.

It was my newborn son who kept me going during those dark days after I gave birth. He brought me tears of laughter and happiness straight into my soul. It's amazing how these little untouched, beautiful and pure creatures shower you with unconditional love. They are untouched by society's ideals. They are completely oblivious to anything. All they want is your warmth, love, smiles, and to win your heart. My son was the only human who did not care about my appearance and because of that I got my heart, my sanity, and happiness back. I bless the day he was born.

Being invisible has been a valuable lesson. For the first time I realized I was invisible to myself. I wasn't present. I was living my life going through the motions. I couldn't see myself beyond my reflection in the mirror. Key is self-awareness and inner happiness. I so very much believe in that. The more you are aware of yourself, the more changes you realize you have to go through. Then something really interesting happens. Everyone else around you is invisible but not you. You are completely whole with yourself.

Believe in yourself and in your first gut instinct. Then you are visible to yourself without doing anything. Just your energy and being you makes you unique. People will be drawn to you like a magnet.

The day I hit 125 pounds closed a circle of big and small achievements.

Previously, I was so perfectly packaged but I left the beauty untouched inside. I finally feel beauty now. I know who the people around me are, the sincere and real ones who truly care. Now I have the confidence to be myself and not fear judgment.

The entire experience has taught me that when I was slim and appealing, I took so much for granted that the things that I really wanted to do ended up in the shallow side of things. What a waste! Today is to appreciate it all.

But the most important lesson of my experience has been the lesson of the unconditional love I learned from my son. He has filled me with neverending joy and light. Truly, the gift of motherhood is one that never stops giving. To those of you out there invisible, take back your life. It's a struggle but it's worth the pain. Life is a game of living. Get busy living.

Smile, smile a lot. It's like my mom would always tell me; smiles don't cost you anything. They are free for the world to see.

It took me eight months but the old appealing image is back, but the person inside is different. There's no vanity, just much more compassion, tolerance, and understanding. Now I demand justice. I appreciate everything I once took for granted and more. I appreciate gestures from other people. It was an amazing journey. I'd gone from looking and feeling sixty years old at 245 pounds to looking thirty and feeling twenty at 125 pounds.

I am an artist. I paint. I sculpt. I sing. I take dance classes, not because I want to be a dancer, but because the movement makes me feel good. I take acting lessons, not because I want to be a movie star, but because it makes me smile and feel alive.

I am not saying go bungee jumping tomorrow, but enjoy every moment. Do something that makes you feel good inside. Believe in yourself and in your first gut instinct. Trust your decisions and then you are visible to yourself and to others without doing anything more than just being uniquely you.

People say that life is full of surprises. Some of them are good and some of them are not so good. It all depends on how you look at it. For me, I don't see good and bad anymore. I believe everything is perfect. That everything that happens, really happens for a reason and leads you to your next destination.

This book is especially for all the women and for all the obese people out there who have gone through and are still going through a similar experience as I did, but are struggling alone. I tell you, there is a way out. There is life. If people discourage you, don't cry the violins. It is a waste of your time and health. You struggle and fight back. Laugh. Make humor out of any tragedy that comes across your path. I have a feeling you will do just fine

My next destination was completely unexpected. One week after I reached my pre-pregnancy weight of 125 pounds, I discovered I was pregnant again. My second pregnancy just happened. It was not planned. I didn't know whether to laugh or to cry. My first instinct was to put a bullet through my husband's and my own head.
Oh well.

Here we go again ....

Tips, Social Dangers, and Rules for Your Diet

Losing weight doesn't mean you have to stay home locked in your closet until you lose the pounds. Go out, enjoy yourself. Live! Just remember it is all about sticking to your diet combined with social protocol. I have a few tips that help.

No, no's!

* No finger food.
* No late dinners. You'll swell like a balloon.
* Now this is a tough one. No alcohol. Can you handle it? Stay away from restaurant soups because of carbohydrates and fats in them.
* No carbohydrates, fried foods, or dairy.
* Red meat only once a week.
* No food after 7:00PM.
* Don't skip meals. Your body is like clockwork, don't torture it or yourself. You will end up losing muscle and not fat. To lose fat you must eat to be able to burn fat.

Don't tell everyone you meet that you are on a diet. Wait until they notice it first. If you mess up one day don't despair, keep going to the next day. It's not the end of your diet. It's just the end of that day. Get right back on it the next morning. Results don't come overnight but once it shows, it really shows.

Don't accept as many invitations to go out to eat. If you do, make it look like you eat; if you don't, it puts too much attention on you. Just chat and chew selectively.

Don't weigh yourself until you feel a big difference in the way your clothes fit. Remember, the scale is your enemy and it's most powerful in the beginning and the end.

Yes, Yes's!

❋ Unlimited water.

❋ Sip unlimited amounts of cold herbal decaffeinated natural tea when you get a craving. Drink after every meal.

❋ Steamed vegetables, (only greens) to "play with" during dinner.

❋ Go out and buy a pair of fabulous new jeans in the size you use to be.

I did and the salesgirl's mouth hung open when I said they were for me. From where she was standing it looked like I was holding a key chain.

Make sure you have lots of support, you'll need it.

Try to fit more walks in your schedule and work yourself slowly into a workout regime.

Set realistic goals and when you achieve one, reward yourself with a massage to release all the toxins.

Do have a drink with you guests. No one likes a party pooper. But fill a fancy glass with ice and a juice with a garnish.

Before bedtime—a lot of water.

When you have successfully lost the weight, go back to the store with your new jeans on and make an entrance. Twirl around the salesgirl.

And most importantly, patience, patience, and more patience! You have to be patient when you are on a diet. Losing weight too fast is not good, you must eat! I promise you this works. It will make you a very happy person.

All
Day
Menus
For the
Willing
Ones

Wake Up Call

fresh-squeezed juice (Don't be lazy, do take out the juicer, it's worth it as it will help you clean your body)

* celery
* cucumber
* ginger
* carrot

Blend: 2 long sticks of celery, 1 big cucumber with skin, ½ pinky size ginger carrot.

1 full cup, drink up!!! all the way, please!

Breakfast

2 slices of Norwegian smoked salmon

(largely devoid of salt)
1 or 2 boiled eggs, depending on how hungry you are. Throw the yellow out (no yoke) and keep the egg white. 2 slices of papaya. Cut 4 or 5 slices of cucumber. Enjoy some mint tea after.

Meat Balls

Ingredients

pound of ground turkey
1 teaspoon of olive oil
1 egg
1 onion (large)
5 garlic cloves
¾ teaspoon of salt
¾ teaspoon of pepper
onion powder (splash around the top)
1 teaspoon of Parmesan cheese

1. Mix all of the ingredients together well by hand.

2. Prepare oven preheated at 375 °F for 45 mins.

3. Preparing the sauce: Mix 1 onion, 5 garlic teeth, and 1 tablespoon of olive oil.

On the stove: Mix 2 cups of water, 3 sliced carrots, 2 yellow squash, 3 zucchini, 1 red pepper, and 1 chicken stock cube.

Cook halfway, then blend it until it turns to liquid, put back in pot, add 1 tomato, small can, ½ jar of marinara sauce, ¼ jar of vodka sauce.

Cook for 10 minutes on medium flame.

Finally, put balls in gently and cook for 5 minutes and serve.

Grilled Salmon

Ingredients

1 salmon steak
teriyaki sauce, low sodium
asparagus, 5
½ cauliflower
1 onion
Dijon mustard
¼ tablespoon of salt
¼ tablespoon of pepper
1 lemon

1. Fill a medium pan with ¾ cup water, bring to boil, add asparagus, lower after boil to medium until asparagus is soft, and to your liking.

2. Pour the sweet soy sauce in a deep dish. Wash the salmon, then rinse and dry it with a paper towel.

3. Place salmon in soya bowl, flip and turn a few times, leave to marinate for 10 minutes in the bowl.

4. Take tin foil, place the salmon on it, add salt and pepper, wrap it well.

5. Put it in a preheated oven for 15 minutes at 375°F.

Blender sauce: Cauliflower+Dijon mustard+ ½ cup of 2% milk Remove asparagus, rinse, and place on plate.

Remove salmon from oven and tin foil, place on plate with the juices from the teriyaki. Pour cauliflower Dijon sauce on asparagus, add a few splashes of lemon on salmon and serve.

Flat–Skirt Steak

Ingredients

4 garlic cloves
1 teaspoon of olive oil
salt (low sodium), splash
red paprika, splash
½ lemon
ginger
carrots
tahini

1. Wash steak and simmer in salt water for 5 minutes.

2. Rinse out and dry with paper towel.

3. Grill the meat each side for 3 minutes on medium flame.

4. Thoroughly mix together 4 chopped garlic cloves, 1 teaspoon of olive oil, a splash of salt, a splash of red paprika.

5. Remove steak and place it on steak, spread the mix on top.

6. Add a squeeze of lemon on top.

String beans:

Fill a pan ¾ with water and bring to a boil, lower the flame to medium, and cook until beans are soft, to your liking.

Drain and put on the plate next to steak.

Dressing for beans: Take 1 inch ginger, 4 large carrots, ½ cup of tahini, ¼ olive oil, and a splash of salt, and mix them in a blender for a few seconds. Pour onto the beans and they are ready to serve.

Grilled Orange Chicken

Ingredients

organic, free-range chicken
4 oranges
salt
pepper-block
honey
yellow and green zucchini
garlic
onion salt
red paprika

1. Rinse chicken.
2. Fill a deep oven pan three-fourths fill with water and place chicken in the middle.
3. Take 3 oranges and squeeze them into water.
4. Take 1 orange, cut, with the peel, and place it around the chicken in the water.
5. Add salt and pepper to your liking.
6. Massage 1 tablespoon of honey into the chicken.
7. Tightly cover with tin foil.
8. Put in preheated oven: 45 minutes, 375°F.

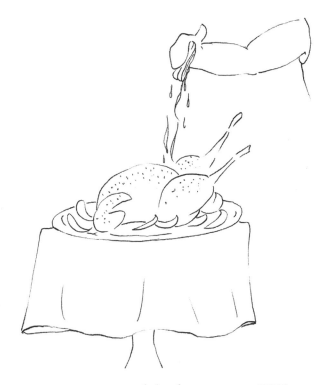

9. Last 15 minutes, remove tin foil and raise temp. to 490°F.

10. Remove chicken from oven, let is stand for 5 minutes, the cut and serve.

Side dish:

Place yellow and green zucchini in oven pan. They should be thinly sliced (potato chips). Add salt, garlic, onion salt, and red paprika. Do not cover. Set oven on bake for 35 minutes on 375°F. Turn over until golden brown and crisp.. When ready, place next to chicken, pour chicken broth on chicken and zucchini and serve!

Vegetarian Dish

Ingredients

scallions
chopped zucchini
squash
flat string beans
green peas
onions
chopped garlic
glass noodles
salt and pepper
paprika or red chili powder
iceberg lettuce
sprouts (the big, thick ones)
mushrooms

1. Bring a pot of water to boil.

2. Gently place the glass noodles inside the pot.

3. Put flame on low for 15 minutes until soft.

4. Drain and put in a frying pan with no oil or butter, nothing.

5. Chop all the vegetables to size you prefer and put in a pot, ¾ full of water.

6. Bring to boil, then lower temperature and cook until soft.

7. While cooking, add salt, pepper, and paprika.

8. If you're into spicy food, you may add a splash of chili powder. (A piece of advice: take it easy on the salt.)

9. Stir and add the noodles.

10. Add chopped garlic.

11. Stir, bring to sizzle, and remove from the stove. Cover for 5 minutes and serve!

Salad

Ingredients

3 color lettuce
cucumber
papaya
hearts of palm
avocado
chicken breast
low fat mayo (no egg mayo)
curry sauce (not creamed)

1. Chop the lettuce to your liking.

2. Chop the cucumbers into cubes.

3. Slice the hearts of palm into thick slices.

4. Chop the avocado into strips.

5. Chop papaya into cubes.

6. Toss and mix all together with 1 tablespoon of olive oil.

On the side:

Grill 1½ pieces of chicken breast on medium flame. Don't add anything and let it cool for 10 minutes. Then chop the chicken into tiny, tiny pieces (shred it if you desire).

Add 1 hefty spoon of no egg mayo. Add 1 hefty spoon of curry sauce. Mix well, place 2 big scoops on top of green salad and serve!

Soup "Vegetable Festival"

Ingredients

any vegetables that you like, but no red vegetables!
soy sauce (low sodium)
tofu block (white) pure
pinto beans
non-fat sour cream
scallions
red pepper

1. Fill large pot with water (¾ full).
2. Add any kind of chopped vegetables you like, except red vegetables.
3. Add pinto beans.
4. Bring to a boil, then put flame on low, and cook until vegetables are soft.
5. Add ½ teaspoon of soy sauce (low sodium) 5 minutes into cooking.
6. Add 1 block of white pure tofu, chopped into cubes.
7. When ready, pour into a serving bowl.
8. With a big spoon, add the non-fat sour cream in the middle.
9. Sprinkle chopped scallions and a dash of red pepper on the sour cream.

❀ Serve!

Try not to snack, but if you must!

2% milk, blueberries, green apples, mint leaves

In blender, blend blueberries, green apple, and mint leaves together with 1 cup of 2% milk. Pour in a cup and serve. This is a great snack to fill up your belly

Then, if you are still hungry, take a non-fat yogurt with mixed dry fruit, mix it all together (pass on the granola, please), and enjoy!

To my Gipsy
Thank you for giving me the best years of your life.
May angels watch over you in heaven.

A special thanks goes to Katharina Otto Bernstein
"my book guru" who has a brilliant mind, endless vision
and experience, and whom I truly admire.
She is a true friend and without her wisdom, advice,
and sincere honesty this book would not look the way
it does. I am so thankful to have her in my life,
which she endlessly enriches.

I would like to extend my heartfelt gratitude to my best
friend Glenda Harvey who showed unrelenting support
and was always there for me with unconditional love.

My loving, caring mother is the reason that
I am able to do what I do today.
Her upbringing has endowed me with the
ability to achieve anything I dream of.
Eternally, her capricorn of love and stability
nurishes my heart.

My husband Calle has without exception
been there for me from first page to last
of the book.

Last, but most certainly nost least, I would like to
thank Max Gross "my little computer whiz"
for putting up with my perfectionism
in my book design.

My Notebook